Poems about FOOD

Compiled by Brian Moses   Artwork by Kelly Waldek

WAYLAND

Titles in the series:

Poems about Food
Poems about School
Poems about Space

Editor: Sarah Doughty
Designer: Tessa Barwick

First published in 1999 by
Wayland Publishers Ltd
61 Western Road, Hove
East Sussex, BN3 1JD

Find Wayland on the Internet at http://www.wayland.co.uk

British Library Cataloguing in Publication Data
Poems about Animals – (Wayland poetry collections)
   1. Animals – Juvenile poetry 2. Children's poetry, English
I. Moses, Brian, 1950 –
821.9'008'0362

ISBN 0 7502 2442 8

Printed and bound by Edições ASA, Portugal

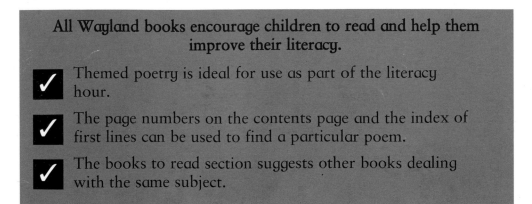

All Wayland books encourage children to read and help them improve their literacy.

✓ Themed poetry is ideal for use as part of the literacy hour.

✓ The page numbers on the contents page and the index of first lines can be used to find a particular poem.

✓ The books to read section suggests other books dealing with the same subject.

Contents

Fruit Feast

Come on children gather round,
Fruit to feast your eye,
Apples and pomegranites
Are such a good buy
Come, taste these grapes,
guavas and mangoes too,
Four at one rupee, just for you.
There are berries, sour and sweet,
And yellow bananas delicious to eat.

Asian Nursery Rhyme

One for the Pineapple

One for the pineapple for our tea.
Two for the plums in the old plum tree.
Three for the empty banana skins.
Four for the peach juice on our chins.
Five for a bunch of bright red cherries.
Six for a handful of ripe blackberries.
Seven for the apples in the pie Dad made.
Eight for the lemons in the lemonade.
Nine for the oranges we squeezed for squash.
Ten for the fingers that need a wash.

John Foster

Yellow Butter

Yellow butter purple jelly red jam
    black bread
Spread it thick
Say it quick
Yellow butter purple jelly red jam
    black bread
Spread it thicker
Say it quicker
Yellow butter purple jelly red jam
    black bread
Now repeat it
While you eat it
Yellow butter purple jelly red jam
    black bread
Don't talk with your mouth full!

Mary Ann Hoberman (USA)

Toast

Want to know what Dad likes most?
BURNT TOAST.

Lightly scorched just will not do,
It should be black the whole way through.

Palest brown? You must be joking –
He isn't happy till it's smoking.

Listen to him crunch and sing
While people cough and fire bells ring.

Now you know what Dad likes most ...
BURNT TOAST.

Clare Bevan

Make your Mind up Mum!

This is the sort of stuff
I get served at meal times –

cereals with free toys and puzzles,
alphabet soup,
pasta monsters and little men,
'Jungle Animal' shaped turkey fries,
green, wobbly jelly ghosts
and ice-cream with dinosaurs right through it,
animal crackers
and football shaped 'World Cup' cakes.

I don't mind
but when my mum's in a bad mood she'll shout
'PHILIP STOP PLAYING WITH YOUR FOOD!'

Philip Waddell

8

Burgers

We can eat burgers
anywhere,
at the barbecue
or at the fair,
at the fast food stall
or the restaurant,
burgers are always
what we want!

Brian Moses

Lunch

Munch, crunch,
Time for lunch:
Eat my chips,
Lick my lips,
Eat my apple,
Leave the pips.

Celia Warren

Sounds Good

Sausage sizzles,
crispbreads crack;
hot dogs hiss
and flapjacks snap!

Bacon boils
and fritters fry;
apples squelch
in apple pie.

Baked beans bubble,
gravy grumbles;
popcorn pops,
and stomach rumbles ...

I'M HUNGRY!

Judith Nicholls

Popcorn Pie

Take a thousand petals,
dew from midnight sky;
a dandelion,
a corn cob
grown in hot July.
Add a pinch of poppyseed,
fan with dragonfly;
sprinkle clover –
now stand back –
Catch your POPCORN PIE!

Judith Nicholls

Sticky Licky

In the summer,
When it's sunny,
Eating ice-cream
Can be funny.

Ice-cream melts
And drips so fast
It's quite hard
To make it last.

It's so lovely,
Sweet and licky,
But when it drips,
You get sticky.

I get ice-cream
on my clothes
In my hair
And up my nose.

My dad says
I should eat less;
Ice-cream plus me
Equals – mess!

Tony Bradman

The Perfect Milkshake

Banana with grated chocolate,
kiwi fruit or pear,
If I made the perfect milkshake
I wouldn't be stopping there ...

I'd add strawberries and melon,
pineapple and toffee,
mix it up with hazelnuts
and a tablespoon of coffee,

all topped with a glacé cherry
and a double squirt of cream,
the taste would be heavenly,
just like drinking a dream!

Brian Moses

Jelly

The jelly comes quivering
Out of the mould
Like someone shivering
From the cold.

It wibbles and wobbles
Round my plate
as if it were learning
To roller-skate.

Then down my throat
I feel it slide
On the slippery slope
To my inside.

Stanley Cook

The Lolly

I hid my lolly
behind the radiator.
There was only a puddle
when I came back later.

Charles Thomson

Noisy Food

When you're munching crunchy apples
or you're slurping up your soup,
when you're eating crackly crisps
all on your own or in a group,
when you're crunching up your cornflakes
or you're popping bubblegum,
or you're sucking at an orange
with such squelches that your mum
says, "Can't you eat more quietly,
that noise is rather rude!"
It's then you say, "It's not my fault.
I'm eating noisy food."

Marian Swinger

Hunger

Home from school.
After four.
Shut the gate.
Close the door.

Raid the fridge.
Search the shelf.
I need food
to fill myself.

Are there biscuits?
Is there bread?
Where's the jam?
I MUST be fed.

Peanut butter!
Lucky me!
That was good.
What's for tea?

Ann Bonner

The Sun is

The sun is a cupcake, with yellow icing,
Rays of bright light float off it
like powdered sugar.
It is as hot as fire,
As it sits in its own oven,
Slowly baking so it is crisp to the touch.

a Cupcake

Gradually the sun gets lower and lower,
until it is only half visible.
Someone has taken a huge bite out
of the cupcake.
The night is having a midnight feast.

Catherine Garnett (aged 11)

Dragon Feast

If you want to feed a dragon,
start with something hot,
spicy prawns in Vindaloo,
the fiercest that you've got.

They like all kinds of fiery food,
red-hot chillies, pickled limes,
sausages in mustard, peppered crab
with toast burned fourteen times.

Follow this with deep-fried mango
in a flaming brandy sauce,
and some of the very strongest mints
to finish with, of course.

Moira Andrew

Buns

Buns in the bakery.
Buns in the bag.
Buns big and bulging.
Buns that sag.

Buns that dribble.
Buns that drip.
Buns as big
as a battleship.

Buns that are smooth.
Buns that are sticky.
Buns fun to munch on,
(but some are quite tricky).

Buns on the table,
piled up for tea.
Buns all buttery.
Buns in me!

Tony Mitton

Potato Poem

I like potatoes
However you cook them,
Whether you've baked them
Or battered or shook them.

Fry them or chip them
Or turn them to mash,
Soak them in sauces
Or mix them with hash.

Serve them up steaming
Or dish them up cold,
Pile them on paper
Or plates made of gold.

Boil them or slice them
Roast them or spike them
Grate them or dice them,
Potatoes –

    I like them!

Clare Bevan

Chips

Out of the paper bag
Comes the hot breath of the chips
And I shall blow on them
To stop them burning my lips.

Before I leave the counter
The woman shakes
Raindrops of vinegar on them
And salty snowflakes.

Outside the frosty pavements
Are slippery as a slide
But the chips and I
Are warm inside.

Stanley Cook

Pies

I spied a pie through the baker's door
And then I spied a whole lot more

Apple pie with crusty topping
Rabbit pie that won't stop hopping
Mince pie hot on Christmas Day
Pigeon pie that flies away
Cottage pie with bricks and mortar
Octopi found underwater
Butcher's pie with steak and kidney
Witches pie with Kate and Sidney
Shepherd's pie with spuds and carrots
Pirate's pie with squawking parrots

Blackbird pie begins to sing
Eel pie keeps on wriggling
Custard pie that someone throws
Mud pie oozing through your toes
Fish pie swimming in the sea
Cherry pie – the one for me!

I spied a pie through the baker's door
A spider pie? Are you really sure?

Paul Bright

Further Information

Following on from any reading of a poem, either individually or in groups, check with the children that they have understood what the poem is about. Ask them to point out any difficult words or lines and explain these. Ask the children how they feel about the poem. Do they like it? Is there a particular section or line in the poem that they particularly enjoy?

The poem 'One for the Pineapple' by John Foster may be used as a model poem for the children's own writing. Some children may enjoy the challenge of getting their poem to rhyme but others may prefer just to concentrate on linking ideas with numbers. Such a poem might be illustrated and made into a big book to share with other classes.

Talk with the children about their favourite foods. Suggest that they make a survey of favourite foods. They can ask other children, teachers, dinner ladies and family members. Then look at the two poems by Clare Bevan, 'Toast' and 'Potato Poem'. Does anyone else on the list have a really odd favourite food like burnt toast?

Use the data from the survey of favourite foods as a starting point for poetry writing. Children might begin their poems in a similar way to Clare Bevan's 'Potato Poem':

> Vanessa likes chips
> piled high on her plate,
> with burgers and beans,
> chips are great.
>
> Mum likes carrots,
> she eats them a lot,
> sliced or grated
> or cooked in a pot.
>
> My teacher likes ...

'Noisy Food' by Marian Swinger is perfect for performance with children making the most of all the onomatopoeic words. As well as pronouncing the words in an interesting way, children could also consider adding sound effects using percussion instruments such as shakers and scrapers, or even home-made or 'found' instruments – crackly crisp packets, autumn leaves in a bag, etc.

Consider 'Popcorn Pie' by Judith Nicholls. Can children write their own recipe poems? This could be linked with 'Dragon Feast' by Moira Andrew and the recipe might be –

Dragon Pie. Would it be filled with hot things? What if the dragon got over-heated? Can children compose a poem for a mixture of foods to cool him down? See Paul Bright's poem 'Pies' for inspiration for other pies which could be made for giants, mermaids, sea monsters and all manner of strange creatures.

Encourage children to look for further poems about food. These can be copied out and then illustrated. Build up a collection of poems and let children talk about their favourites. Let them practise reading and performing the poems.

Such activities as these will promote and reinforce the suggested work at various levels in the National Literacy Strategy.

About the Poets

Moira Andrew used to be a primary headteacher and a College of Education lecturer. She is now a full-time writer and poet in schools. Sometimes she writes about her family and her cats. She says "The cats don't mind, but the family members sometimes do!"

Clare Bevan lives in Crowthorne, Berkshire with her husband, son and two cats. She used to be a junior school teacher but she now writes children's stories and poems instead. Her favourite hobby is acting.

Ann Bonner lives in the West Midlands. She has been a teacher and writer for the last thirty-five years. She currently works as a writer in schools and a teacher of people with learning difficulties.

Tony Bradman lives in Beckenham. He is probably best known for his 'Dilly the Dinosaur' books but he has also written and edited many others including *The Frankenstein Teacher* (Corgi).

Paul Bright has been living and working in the Netherlands for the last ten years. He has two grown-up children and has been writing ever since they first asked for a bedtime story.

Stanley Cook (1922-91) was born in a small Yorkshire village but spent most of his adult life in Sheffield. He taught at grammar schools and a College of Further

Education. He wrote for adults as well as children, usually about the things he saw around him. He said he hoped that everyone could enjoy his poems.

John Foster taught English for over twenty years. He has edited numerous collections of poetry for children and has had eight books of his own poetry published. He lives in Oxfordshire and regularly visits schools and libraries to perform his poems.

Tony Mitton lived abroad for much of his early childhood. He read English at Cambridge University and then qualified as a teacher. He lives in Cambridge and his latest book of poetry for children is called *Plum* (Scholastic).

Brian Moses lives on the coast in Sussex with his wife and two daughters. He writes and edits books for children and travels the country performing his poems. His latest anthology *The Worst Class in School* is published by Wayland.

Judith Nicholls has worked full-time as a writer since her first book appeared in 1985. She has now written over forty books and has had poems published in over 300 anthologies. She has lived in an ancient cottage in a Wiltshire churchyard for many years.

Marian Swinger lives beside the River Thames not far from London. Her work appears in many anthologies but although she enjoys writing poetry, she makes her living as a photographer.

Charles Thomson lives in London and has been a full-time poet since 1987. He has visited over 700 schools and broadcast his poems on radio and television. His work is in over eighty anthologies.

Philip Waddell is Guyanese born of Portuguese stock. He has lived in Australia and Bangladesh as well as in England. He enjoys travelling and loves all sorts of food except rhubarb.

Celia Warren lives in Staffordshire with her husband, children, dog, guinea pig, hamster and goldfish who have all appeared in poems that she has written. When she writes her poems she keeps reading them out loud. Her dog thinks that she is talking to herself and looks sorry for her.

Picture acknowledgements Tony Stone Images 11 (Chris Everard).

Books to Read

Mrs. Wobble the Waitress and **Master Bun the Baker's Boy**. Both of these books are written by Allan Ahlberg as part of the 'Happy Families' series (Puffin). They are great fun and lovely reads for newly independent readers.

The Very Hungry Caterpillar by Eric Carle (Puffin picture book). This is the tale of a caterpillar who eats his way through the book consuming a variety of food on the way. A real joy for any age.

Hedgehogs Don't Eat Hamburgers by Vivienne French (Puffin, Ready, Steady, Read Series). Hector and Hattie and Harry and Hester are looking for a juicy hamburger while Fox and Badger are hoping to find four hedgehogs to eat!

The Rascally Cake by Jean Willis, with illustrations by Korky Paul (Puffin). An award-winning picture book in which an especially-revolting cake tries to eat the awful man who made it!

The Dinosaur's Packed Lunch by Jacqueline Wilson (Doubleday). When Dinah drinks a few drops of green liquid from a dinosaur's packed lunch something very odd happens to her.

Tasty Poems compiled by Jill Bennet (Oxford University Press). A small collection of poems about food for the 4-plus age range.

Pizza by Brian Moses (Wayland). A National Curriculum Book List title which explains where pizza ingredients come from and how they are made.

Permissions
The compiler and publisher would like to thank the authors for allowing their poems to appear in this anthology. While every attempt has been made to gain permissions and provide an up-to-date biography, in some cases this has not been possible and we apologise for any omissions.

'One for the Pineapple' © 1998 John Foster from *Bouncing Ben and other Rhymes* (OUP) included by permission of the author; 'The Sun is a Cupcake' by Catherine Garnett from *Wondercrump Poetry* by permission of Random House, Ltd.

Index of First Lines